Garfield

Pick Of The Bunch

JIM DAVIS

W9-BAO-367

ℛℛ
RAVETTE PUBLISHING

First published by Ravette Books Limited 1993
Reprinted by Ravette Publishing Limited 1995,
1996 (twice), 1999

Printed and bound in Great Britain
for Ravette Publishing Limited,
Unit 3, Tristar Centre,
Star Road, Partridge Green,
West Sussex RH13 8RA
by Cox & Wyman Ltd, Reading, Berkshire

ISBN 1 85304 258 7

© 1991 United Feature Syndicate, Inc.

© 1991 United Feature Syndicate, Inc.

© 1991 United Feature Syndicate, Inc

I SEE THE "STRANGE MICE" ARE BACK

JIM DAVIS 11-9

JIM DAVIS 11-13

© 1991 United Feature Syndicate, Inc.

JIM DAVIS 11-14

JiM DAViS 11-21

JIM DAVIS 11-25

© 1991 United Feature Syndicate, Inc.

© 1991 United Feature Syndicate, Inc

© 1991 United Feature Syndicate, Inc.

© 1991 United Feature Syndicate, Inc.

© 1991 United Feature Syndicate, Inc.

JIM DAVIS 12-12

© 1991 United Feature Syndicate, Inc.

© 1991 United Feature Syndicate, Inc.

BEWARE
OF DOG

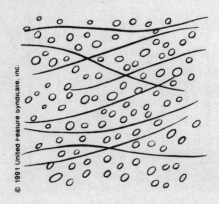

© 1991 United Feature Syndicate, Inc.

FINALLY... A NICE, PEACEFUL MEAL

© 1992 United Feature Syndicate, Inc.

CRUNCH!

HAVE YOU SEEN MY LUCKY ROCK?

YES, YES, THE EXCITEMENT LEVEL OF THIS ROOM ROSE DRAMATICALLY UPON MY ARRIVAL

JIM DAVIS 1-17

© 1992 United Feature Syndicate, Inc.

© 1992 United Feature Syndicate, Inc.

JIM DAVIS 2-18

© 1992 United Feature Syndicate, Inc.

JIM DAVIS 2-21

© 1992 United Feature Syndicate, Inc.

JIM DAVIS 2-26

I WONDER IF OTHER PEOPLE'S PETS HAVE WILD MOOD SWINGS?

GRRRR   GRRRR

© 1992 United Feature Syndicate, Inc.

© 1992 United Feature Syndicate, Inc.

NEXT TRIP YOU'RE RIDING IN THE TRUNK

© 1992 United Feature Syndicate, Inc.

© 1992 United Feature Syndicate, Inc.

OTHER GARFIELD BOOKS AVAILABLE

Classics @ £4.99 each   ISBN
Volume One   1 85304 970 0
Volume Two   1 85304 971 9

Miscellaneous
Garfield Treasury   £9.99   1 85304 975 1

Garfield Address & Birthday   1 85304 918 2
Book Gift Set   £7.99 inc VAT

Garfield 21st Birthday   1 85304 995 6
Celebration Book   £9.99

All Ravette books are available at your local bookshop or from the address below. Just tick the titles required and send the form with your payment to:-

BBCS, P O Box 941, Kingston upon Hull HU1 3YQ
24-hour telephone credit card line 01482 224626
Prices and availability are subject to change without notice.
Please enclose a cheque or postal order made payable to BBCS to the value of the cover price of the book and allow the following for postage and packing:

UK & BFPO: £1.95 (weight up to 1kg)   3-day delivery
              £2.95 (weight over 1kg up to 20kg)   3-day delivery
              £4.95 (weight up to 20kg)   next day delivery

EU & Eire:	Surface Mail	£2.50 for first book & £1.50 for subsequent books
	Airmail	£4.00 for first book & £2.50 for subsequent books
USA:	Surface Mail	£4.50 for first book & £2.50 for subsequent books
	Airmail	£7.50 for first book & £3.50 for subsequent books
Rest of	Surface Mail	£6.00 for first book & £3.50 for subsequent books
the World:	Airmail	£10.00 for first book & £4.50 for subsequent books

Name ....

Address ....

....

....

Cards accepted: Visa, Mastercard, Switch, Delta, American Express

Expiry Date.........................Signature ....